The Usborne Christmas Patterns to Colour

Designed and illustrated by
Nayera Everall

Written by
Kirsteen Rogers

Additional illustration by
Ruth Russell

First published in 2011 by Usborne Publishing Ltd. 83-85 Saffron Hill, London ECIN 8RT, England.
Copyright ©2011 Usborne Publishing Ltd. The name Usborne and the devices 🔆 🎈 are Trade Marks of
Usborne Publishing Ltd.
 Printed in Dongguan, Guangdong, China.

How to use this book

On some of the pages you'll find suggestions for how to colour the patterns, but it's your book and you can do whatever you like.

If you'd like to cut out your pattern, you'll find a dotted line on each page to cut along.

Use pens, crayons or pencils to fill the patterns. You can colour the designs as they are or draw more patterns in some of the shapes. You could try...

...spots and dots...

...zigzags and stripes...

...snowflakes...

...or stars.

You could fill the shapes on this page with some of your own pattern ideas.

To fill in large areas like this use lots of lines going in the same direction.

The colour suggestion panels have dotted lines so you can cut them off if you want to. The white shapes are there in case you'd like to try out colour ideas of your own before you begin.

It's a good idea to lay your book on a firm, flat surface while you are colouring.

You could use these colours:

Or try these:

Or use these circles for your own ideas:

2

Choosing colours

This bright ring is a colour wheel and you can use it to help you pick colours that will go well together or create particular effects.

Colours at the edge of the wheel are darker. They get paler towards the middle.

The wheel shows the primary colours red, yellow and blue, and a range of colours in between.

The reds, oranges and yellows on the right of the wheel have a warm, comforting character.

Yellow

Colour wheel

Blue

Red

Colours on the left of the wheel, such as purples, blues and greens, have a cool, wintery feel to them.

Colours on opposite sides, such as pink and green, go well together and make each other seem brighter.

Creating different effects

Reds, green and yellows are traditional Christmassy colours that give an energetic feel.

You can create a gentle, calm effect using colours that are next to each other on the wheel.

To make a pattern feel 'warm' choose colours from the right of the colour wheel.

For a cool or icy effect, use shades from the left of the colour wheel.

For extra impact, fill some parts of a pattern with black, and leave other areas white.

Using only the primary colours red, yellow and blue will give your patterns extra zing.

5

You could see how this pattern looks in icy colours.

How about using just black, white and silvery greys?

Stark colour suggestions:

For this one, you could use different shades of green.

Some greens
you could try:

Use whatever colours you like for this pattern.

You can try out
your colours here:

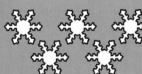

17

Use these colours for a traditional feel:

These will look bold and dramatic:

Or create a new colour combination:

You could fill this pattern with a selection of Christmassy colours.

Or choose colours that sit in the same segment of the wheel, and tone well.

Why not try black and white with two colours?

Use any colours you like to fill this pattern.

You could use these colours:

How about a dramatic look in just black and white?

Or test out some other colour ideas:

27

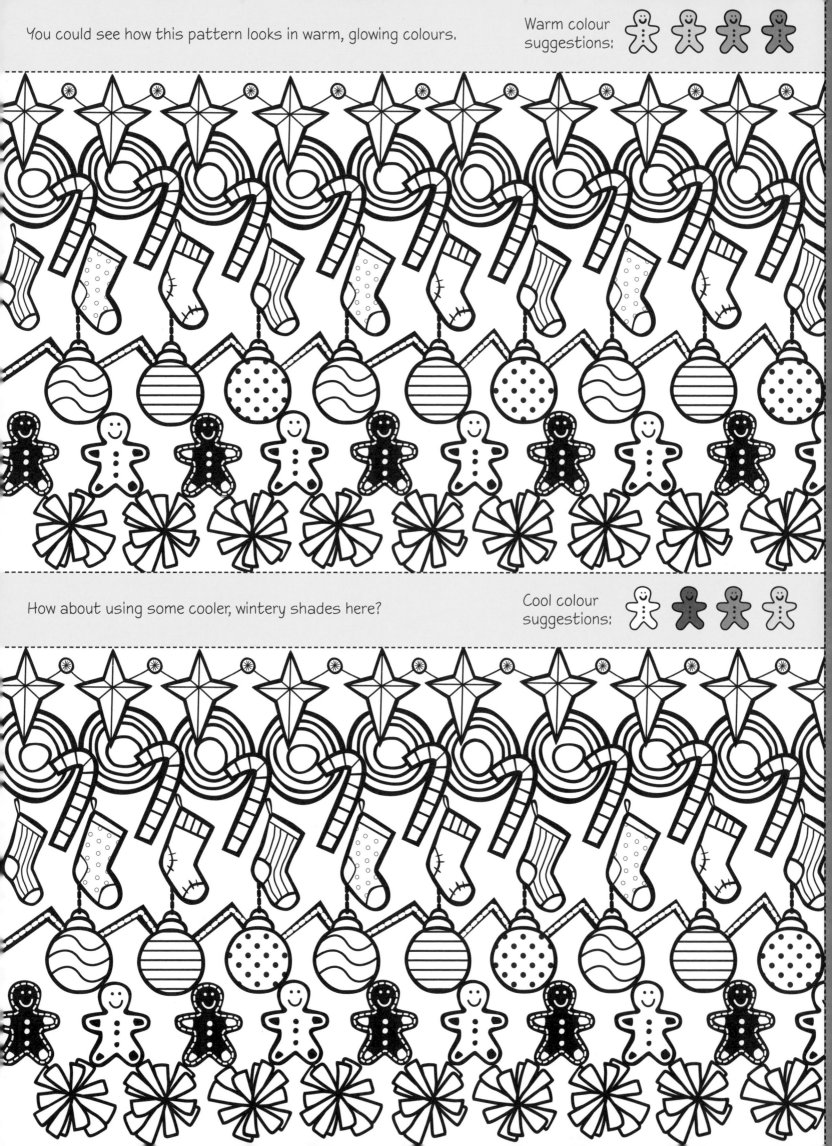

You could see how this pattern looks in warm, glowing colours.

Warm colour suggestions:

How about using some cooler, wintery shades here?

Cool colour suggestions:

For this one, you could pick out some contrasting colours.

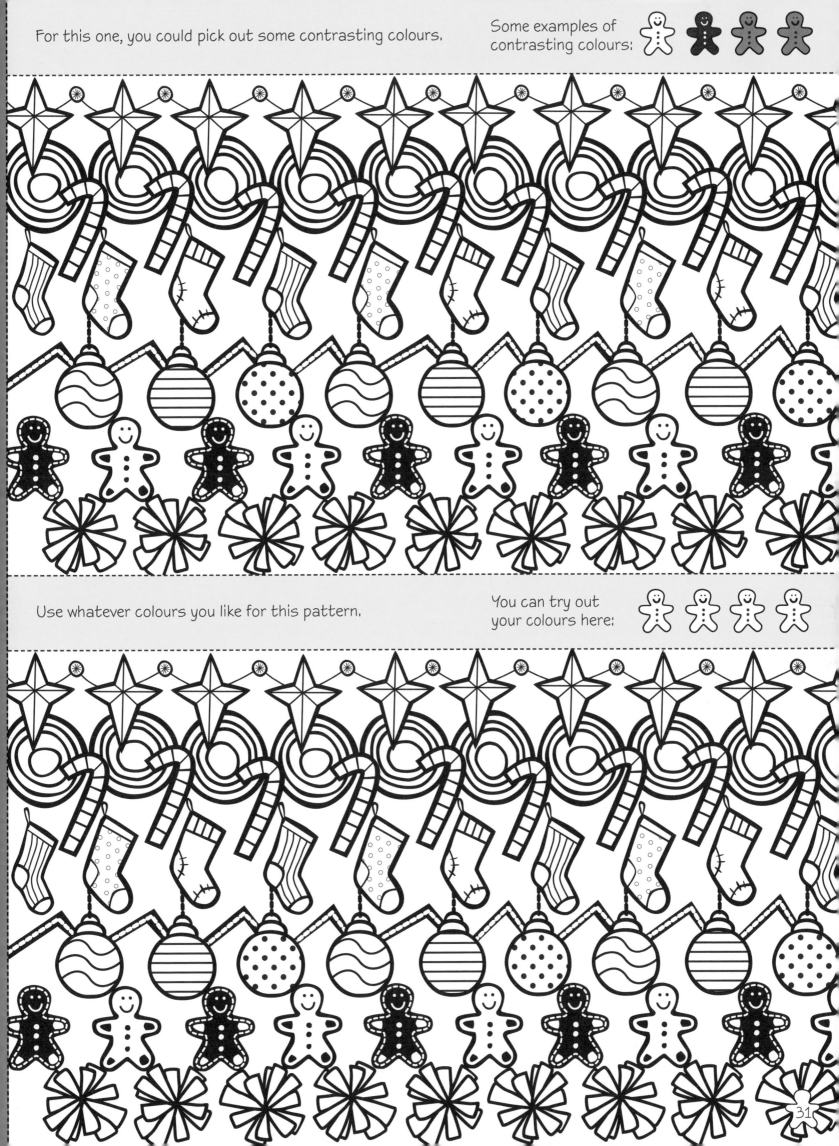

Use whatever colours you like for this pattern.

You can try out your colours here:

31